EDWAR

# *Discovering*
# Bird Courtship

SHIRE PUBLICATIONS LTD

ACKNOWLEDGEMENTS

I am very grateful to my friends who have presented me with photographs to illustrate this book: Jeffery Boswall (Magellanic Penguins, plate 8); Norman Chaffer (Golden and Satin Bowerbirds, plates 11, 12 and 15); Derrick England (Rufous Bush Robin, Black and White Manakin, plates 2 and 9); Tom Lowe (Royal Spoonbills, plate 14); Don V. Merton, New Zealand Wildlife Service (Kakapo, plate 1). The Lyrebird photograph (plate 10) was taken by Cliff Bottomley and presented by the Australian Information Service. Niall Rankin photographed the Wandering Albatrosses (plate 5) and John Warham the Australian Gannets (plate 3), the Grey-headed and Royal Albatrosses (plates 4 and 6) and the Greater Bowerbirds (plate 13). The photograph of the Black Guillemots (plate 7) is my own.

The line drawings are also by me.

The drawing on the cover depicts a male Jackson's Whydah displaying to a female and is by R. A. Hume. It is inspired by photographs kindly given me by Dr V. D. van Someren.

My wife's help has been invaluable.

 *First published 1978. No. 236 in the 'Discovering' series. ISBN 0 85263 415 3.* 

Printed in Great Britain by C. I. Thomas & Sons (Haverfordwest) Ltd, Press Buildings, Merlins Bridge, Haverfordwest, Dyfed.

# Contents

# Introduction

The word 'courtship' is so associated with amorous human relationships that some critics may consider its use in connection with birds unscientific and misleading. They could say, with some justification, that its use suggests similarities with human behaviour which do not exist, but for those who enjoy watching birds and would like to know more about the significance of their activities the use of familiar terms makes it easier to describe and understand their behaviour. Like us birds sing, mimic, build and show off. Ornithologists naturally refer to birds greeting, caressing or intimidating one another. We know little about birds' inner feelings but we have no right to assume that when they behave as we do they do not experience, to however minimal an extent, something that can be described in our usual language.

Ethology, as the study of behaviour is now called, has made rapid advances. It relies on what an animal, whether a bird or some other living creature, is actually recorded as doing, and ethologists commonly use such terms as 'mechanism', 'releaser' or 'trigger' to describe aspects of a bird's behaviour. This is natural and proper as we live in a mechanised culture and think in these terms to a great extent; but to do so is nothing new. The French philosopher Descartes (1596-1650) wrote: 'The animals act naturally and by springs, like a watch.' He commented that they have no feelings — an unwarrantable assumption. Even today some ornithologists too readily regard behaviour as explicable in terms of automatic responses but anyone who has studied a species for a lifetime knows that tomorrow he may see an individual behaving in an unexpected way. A sympathy with birds as lovely, fascinating creatures adds immensely to the enjoyment to be gained from studying them as well as to the ability to interpret their behaviour.

The bird-watcher starts with 'What bird is that?' and even the experienced ornithologist has to ask himself this question frequently when in unfamiliar country. There is great satisfaction in identifying a bird new to your list. The next question, 'What is it doing?' may or may not be easy to answer. But the most interesting question is 'Why is it doing it?' This leads on to queries about a bird's characteristics, its structure, its foraging behaviour, pair-bond, displays, dispersal or migration — a fascinating quest because we find ourselves intrigued by the complex web of adaptations which constitutes the life-style of every species. Each of us can delve just as deeply as he or she pleases into the peculiarities and mysteries of bird behaviour, but, above all, we watch birds because to do so is enjoyable — it is good fun.

# 1. Recognition

**Recognition of habitat**

'Never the time and place and the loved one all together' sums up failure and disappointment in human relationships, and, if we substitute 'potential partner' for 'loved one', disaster among birds. We are so accustomed to the regular appearance of Swallow and Cuckoo that we marvel insufficiently at the readiness of birds to travel thousands of miles to find a mate in a habitat very different from that in which they have wintered. As I watched Swallows skimming over migrating herds of zebra and wildebeest in Tanzania I could not help wondering whether I might next see one of them in Cambridge. A bird reared the previous year with only a few months experience of the appropriate breeding habitat has to be able to recognise it quickly on migrating northwards. A Corncrake mistaking a reed-bed for a grass field would not get a mate.

Most male migrants arrive about ten days or a fortnight before the females and busy themselves 'annexing territory', to use the term introduced by Edmund Selous in 1901. They sing, defend it and are able to receive and court a female with little or no delay. This is of great importance if their progeny are to be fit enough to fly to Africa in the autumn. Females, hearing a male of their own species, recognise his call or song and drop down near to him. Some species, such as the Nightingale and Corncrake, are vocal by night as well as by day so that they can attract potential partners whenever they fly in. Each species has its suitable nesting habitat, more or less restricted. The Sugar Bird of South Africa roams about when not breeding but always nests where a particular plant (*Protea*) is in blossom.

Matters are simpler for resident birds as most of them are in or near suitable habitats. Some which gather in flocks during the winter, such as the Great Tit, may pair up before they disperse.

**Recognition of species**

Birds usually have little difficulty in recognising others of their own species but there are exceptions, due, at least sometimes, to the strength of an individual's sexual or social drive. The Red-necked Phalarope is unusual in that the roles of the sexes are, in many respects, reversed. The female occupies territory and may, at first, approach birds of other species, even those as different as Lapland Buntings. Next she makes advances to birds of her own species, whether male or female, and eventually sex recognition takes place and chases occur. A high level of ardour or excitement in individuals of some species may arouse inappropriate reactions; thus a furious bird may even display aggressively at a man instead of its adversary. Hybrids which occur occasionally between closely related species are usually due to the absence of an individual of a bird's own species and opposite sex. Highly stimulated birds may copulate with some inanimate object and individuals brought up as pets may become 'imprinted' on their keeper and even attempt coition with a human hand.

**Recognition of sex**

Just as we cannot tell at a glance the sex of a Robin or Herring Gull so it can be with the birds themselves, except when, as is often the case, one or other has distinctive adornments or reveals its sex by its song or calls. A male Blackbird is recognisable in spring by his orange bill and a cock Chaffinch by being more brightly coloured than the female; the sex of birds similar in plumage is revealed by their behaviour. When a stranger appears in a male's territory his first response may be, and often is, aggressive. Only after he is reassured by the bird's appearance, behaviour, or both, may courtship begin. Once I placed a mounted, stuffed Wren in a male's territory and when he noticed it he approached to within a foot, sang a congested, aggressive song at it and then copulated. Non-aggressive response — inactivity — was the signal that he was not dealing with another male.

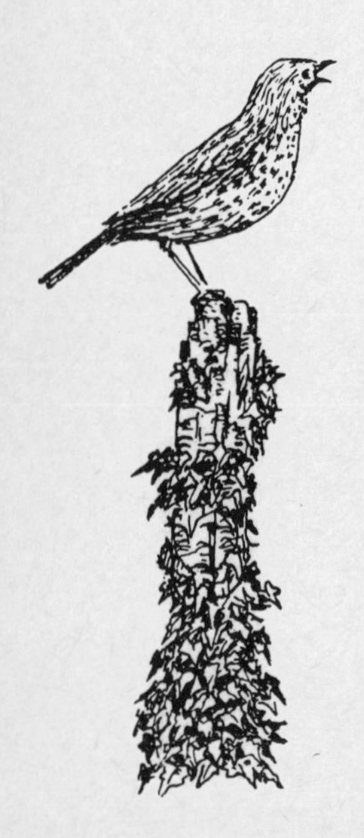

*Fig. 1. Song Thrush singing his territorial song.*

**Features contributing to sex recognition**

The importance of a single characteristic in enabling some birds to identify the sex of another individual was shown by experiments on a Flicker, an American species of woodpecker which has feather tufts resembling a moustache at the base of the male's bill. A mated female was given an artificial 'moustache', with the result that the male no longer recognised her but pursued his bewildered mate as if she were a trespassing male.

**Recognition by the Snow Bunting**

To illustrate recognition and pairing up when male and female are differently adorned, mention may be made of the behaviour of the Snow Bunting, a species nesting sparsely in the Scottish Highlands and with which I became acquainted in Iceland. The black and white plumage of the cock in the breeding season makes him readily distinguishable from the hen. When another Snow Bunting enters a male's territory he squats in a threatening posture uttering a *peee* call — an enquiry as well as a threat. If the newcomer is another male he becomes aggressive and sparring begins, but if the individual is a female she potters around undeterred. Then the cock's motivation becomes sexual; turning his back on her and holding himself upright — the opposite of a threat posture — he spreads his black and white wings, making the most of their showy appearance, and so indicates that she is welcome. He runs about and poses while the hen nonchalantly pecks here and there in the low herbage — a signal of acquiescence and intimation that she is resolving the conflict between the impulses to flee and to stay. Probably such coy behaviour augments the male's ardour. Soon they are pecking about together — pair-formation has been accomplished. Un-

*Fig. 2. Snow Bunting's invitation display.*

mated males sing vigorously but a newly paired male ceases to sing. He disregards an intruding female but she is attacked by his mate.

**Individual recognition**

The cock Snow Bunting is soon able to distinguish his partner from other Snow Buntings. As a general rule paired birds identify each other by minute characteristics. A brooding Swift recognises an intruder if he merely pokes his head into the nesting crevice and a brooding Jackdaw can distinguish her mate by his call amidst the clamour of the flock. A Merlin will leave the nest to join her mate calling in the forest a thousand yards away.

# 2. Coloration, adornment and structure

Only brief reference to this topic is possible here. As with the details of birds' songs, the significance of their adornments, which constitute signals, coloured and shaped, is normally evident to the individuals to whom they are relevant. Thus time is not wasted in futile courtship activities and hybridisation is avoided.

**The significance of conspicuous coloration**

Sober coloration is an advantage in that it conceals a bird from predators; consequently bright plumage and conspicuous adornments could not have evolved had not their advantages outweighed their disadvantages. They aid identification, serve as signals and are often stimulatory. Extremes in coloration occur in fish and insects but are as great or greater among birds. Many of our small, vulnerable birds are inconspicuously coloured but camouflage is most extreme in species such as the Nightjar and Woodcock which spend most of the day quiescent.

Both sexes of the Greater and Lesser Woodpecker are clothed in vivid, contrasting hues but the Green Woodpecker is less conspicuous. The former generally keep to the woods and are adept at dodging among branches whereas the Green often comes into the open to feed on ants and other small creatures and is then not easily seen among the herbage. Amidst dense vegetation pairs of birds keep in touch visually or by making sounds, usually vocal but sometimes instrumental, as with the drumming of woodpeckers. Significantly the Green, being less confined to woodland, utters a loud 'yaffle' and only rarely drums. Compared with these the Wryneck, a relative, is cryptically coloured, feeds largely on the ground, utters a shrill *quee, quee, quee* and, being without a powerful beak, displays aggressively with mouth wide open exhibiting the pink interior. The Frogmouth's threat display is similar.

*Fig. 3. Frogmouth's gaping threat display.*

In some species, such as the Eider Duck, the male, who is predominantly white, is far more conspicuous than his brown mate, who broods in the herbage and is not easily perceived by a predator. The most brilliantly hued European species, among them the Kingfisher, Bee-eater and woodpeckers, in which both sexes are brightly coloured and both take shares in incubation, nest in holes in vertical banks or tree-trunks out of reach of most predators. Their long pointed beaks are an additional deterrent. Species which gain a measure of protection by nesting in high trees, such as Rooks, or on cliffs or islands, commonly have mainly black or white plumage, which, being conspicuous, facilitates the concentration of numbers where a few have found a temporary source of food or an intruder to be mobbed. In Iceland I have seen a sheep which had strayed close to a nesting colony of Arctic Terns driven away by birds diving viciously at it. When close to such a colony it is advisable to hold an arm over one's head to avoid being pecked.

The Bee-eater is probably the most conspicuous European vari-coloured bird, because, unlike the brilliantly hued Kingfisher, numbers fly about in the open around their nesting colonies. The species survives not only because of its hole-nesting and its extreme agility in flight but because its flesh is found by predators to be very distasteful. Thus the pair cuddle together conspicuously and copulate on a perch near the nest-hole. Similarly woodpeckers, which spiral rapidly in courtship flight and dodge nimbly around tree-trunks, are in little danger from predators.

Many of the trees in tropical rain forests are topped by a dense canopy, gay with bright blossoms amidst which brilliantly

*Fig. 4. The elegant Motmot.*

coloured birds are not as conspicuous as might be assumed. The Motmots of tropical America are not only beautifully coloured but have long tails from which some of the barbs of the two longest feathers have been preened or worn away. While perched they swing the tail from side to side. Perhaps the resemblance to a swinging leaf serves to deflect attention from the bird itself, which also, like its relative the Bee-eater, nests in holes.

**Spectacular and sudden displays**

An unexpected display can be particularly effective either to deter or to stimulate sexually. When alarmed the Blue-fronted Amazon Parrot abruptly spreads its wings, exhibiting the blue frontal fringes and normally concealed areas on its flight and tail feathers. Among mammals, reptiles and insects unexpected enlargement of contour is used to intimidate.

Where can a bird keep vivid colour more conveniently available for abrupt disclosure than in its mouth? I have been intrigued and amused to see a Red-breasted Merganser on an Irish lough suddenly favour the duck with an immense yawn, exhibiting the bright red lining of his mandibles — a courtship gesture comparable with that of the female Cormorant who lures her mate by suddenly displaying the bright yellow interior of her bill. The coloured gapes of many nestlings also encourage the rapid delivery of food. The Blue-footed Booby prances around exhibiting his decorative feet, thrusting out his chest, raising his wings slightly and giving vent to a high-pitched whistle. He may pick up a feather and shake his head vigorously while holding it. The female responds by raising her neck feathers and wings. A displaying Frigatebird inflates a large crimson throat sac while rattling his bill against it and making drumming sounds.

The Great Bustard transforms himself into a billowy mass of white feathers with pouch distended and breast lowered close to the ground; Pectoral Sandpipers fly up over the tundra with throats inflated, hovering like little yellow balloons. The male Peacock Pheasant stands with his huge ocelli-adorned plumes raised fanwise towards the female. The most familiar extravagantly adorned bird is the Peacock, strutting and turning, showing off his immense fan of eyed plumes and rattling the quills when the comparatively dowdy female is near. Darwin described the display of the Argus Pheasant. The male circles the female, stops and suddenly raises his huge ocellated plumes, bringing

*Fig. 5. Cormorant's gaping display.*

*Fig. 6. Young Cormorant feeding from parent's gullet.*

them forward over his head. Thus among birds the eye-design is sexually stimulatory while among insects it is intimidatory — there are butterflies, moths and mantids which display 'eyed' wings to deter predators.

**Flushing and eye changes**

The rush of blood to the surface of the skin in consequence of excitement is characteristic of some monkeys and apes as well as man — and also of various birds during sexual display. Among birds which 'blush' are the Bataleur Eagle, Jungle Fowl and Turkey. Bulwer's Pheasant distends the blue wattles around his face and erects his tail in two halves sideways, providing full scope for the wattles to impress the female. The cock Ostrich displays squatting on the ground, moving from side to side, exhibiting his white wing plumes. The skin on the front of his legs and neck momentarily glows bright red.

In the breeding season the legs of the Black-crowned Night Heron acquire a bright pink tint and when a female approaches a displaying male in his territory he lowers his head sideways and grunts, erecting the feathers on crown, neck and back. His eyeballs protrude from their sockets, exposing the red iris. He bows again and parts his mandibles, conveying his pacific intentions. When she enters the nest-site or nest both birds nibble each other's feathers — a feature of displays by species as different as parakeets, penguins, spoonbills and gannets (plates 3 and 14). As in many other related species there is a transition from aggressive to appeasing and invitatory displays.

*Fig. 7. Cormorant's threat display.*

**The significance of structure in displays**

Incidental mention has been and will be made of the importance of structural features in a bird's displays but special attention must be called to the relationship between the character of a bird's bill and its courtship displays. Birds with powerful, pointed or massive beaks tend to posture so that it is evident that threat is not intended; they bow, point their beaks upward simultaneously, neb, preen each other, turn their necks away or even intertwine them and utter specific calls (plates 3, 4, 14). Only when a bird is testing out another does it use threat or threat-like postures and these may be modified into courtship activities. Thus birds' beaks, though adapted for foraging, influence their courtship displays and the nature of the pair-bond. Puffins' bills are primarily adapted for carrying a number of small fish to their chicks (fig. 8) but become highly coloured and enlarged during the breeding season when male and female rattle them together during courtship. The Avocet, which feeds by skimming the surface of pools with its fine upturned bill (fig. 9), tucks it away in a sleeping posture during altercations. No damage to this exceptionally delicate structure is risked. Wandering Albatrosses face one another with wings outspread in mutual display (plate 5) and clatter their beaks together, each sometimes placing its beak under one wing, sometimes under the other. This twisting backwards of the neck, characteristic of White Storks and Cormorants (figs. 16 and 17), has evolved into an instrumental courtship call in some ducks; for example, the Sheldrake produces a rippling sound by rubbing his bill along his wing quills.

The relationship between food supply, courtship display and pair-bond will be discussed later but here mention may be made of how bill-size affects the social organisation and breeding behaviour of one particular species, the Grey-crowned Babbler of

*Fig. 8. Puffin carrying sand eels to its young.*

Australia, which lives in small flocks consisting of one breeding pair and a number of younger birds which cooperate with the pair's domestic activities until they come into breeding condition themselves when about four years old. These less mature birds can be identified by their relatively short bills. Such bands of Babblers are able to live amicably in a common territory probably because the younger birds, equipped with smaller beaks, live on rather different prey from their elders. Perhaps this may also apply to the Groove-billed Ani of the West Indies, which has rather similar communal behaviour: I was surprised to find a pile of eggs in a nest in Trinidad but found out later that this species also lives communally and more than one female may lay in a nest.

*Fig. 9. Avocet feeding.*

# 3. The pair-formation of some British birds

Lest it should seem that naturalists must visit faraway places to see beautiful and fascinating courtship displays here are some brief descriptions of pair-formation among common British species. The courtship of some less familiar birds is described later. The descriptions have been condensed and generalised to some extent and so represent these and other displays as simpler and less varied than they are. Although standardised patterns of behaviour occur, a bird-watcher can always hope to observe something unusual. As bird activity is greatest around dawn he may be well rewarded by rising early.

It is not always easy to determine when pair-formation is complete. Birds may associate without actually being paired and when a cold spell occurs in spring what seem to be pairs may break up and re-form later. Late in the breeding season pairing may be achieved more rapidly than earlier. We have to be careful in jumping to conclusions. Some Starlings seem to pair up in autumn, others not until spring, but during autumn and winter many continental birds visit Britain and observers may fail to detect the differences in beak coloration by which they may be distinguished.

**The pair-formation of Robins**

Soon after dawn a Robin may be seen feeding near a male's territory and gradually edging towards it and over the border. She sings a little — for females sing and defend territory in winter. The cock, perched on a branch singing, chases the intruder, displaying his red breast aggressively, swaying back and forth, but as she does not reply with a similar threat display he flits away and sings vigorously. The female persists, utters another brief song and advances towards him. Again he retreats and sings, as if perplexed by the situation. She is revealing herself as a potential partner partly by what she does and partly by what she does not do. Both are finding difficulty in reconciling their aggressive and sexual impulses.

The assumption that among birds the male chooses his partner is mistaken, for often it is not so. Territory-owning cock birds do not go wandering around looking for mates but wait for females to visit them. Even when they do so all may not go smoothly. Several Whitethroats may visit a singing and displaying cock in succession without pairing with him. We cannot say that he is at fault; they are just not in the sexual condition to respond to one another.

After a period during which the cock Robin sings softly and follows the female around they may appear to take no notice of each other but it may be observed that the male recognises her, even at a distance, possibly by her appearance as well as by her movements. Only after an 'engagement' period of two or three months does the hen build the nest. About this time her mate starts bringing her items of food and a stage is reached when the male mounts her without ceremony.

**Blackbird pair-formation**

The mature cock Blackbird is distinguishable by his bright yellow beak and glossy black plumage, both of which become more pronounced in spring. He struts in front of the female with bill partly open, uttering a quiet, congested song, contrasting with his melodious soliloquising late in the season and rather similar to the imperfect utterance of early spring, then usually heard from low in a bush. He stretches out his neck, erecting its feathers and those on his body, also fanning his lowered tail, advancing repeatedly a few steps, bowing his head and making excited turning movements. When there are signs that she is acquiescent he adopts a pose with half-opened bill raised and plumage compressed. In the pair-formation and mating displays of many birds such responses indicate that reconciliation is occurring between conflicting impulses. When posturing on a branch a Blackbird may merely stoop to touch it momentarily with his bill but in fighting mood he wipes it, as many other birds do — a type of irrelevant or 'displacement' activity.

As described later, some birds when in a state of inner conflict may peck at the ground without actually feeding, pick up twigs or even attack an irrelevant or inanimate object, but only once have I seen a display which can be regarded as a variation of this kind of displacement activity. Frequently two cock Blackbirds appeared from the shrubberies at either side of a lawn and one would pick up large withered leaves, brandish them on high and advance towards the other. They went back and forth without any actual clash occurring — I was reminded of banner-bearing demonstrators. I can recall no other similar belligerent display though agitated birds may pick up and throw down leaves or other objects, including feathers, but courting birds may brandish objects to augment their display. An Australian Red and Black Wren, flirting with a female, was seen to pluck a petal from a red canna and, holding it by the stem, wave it in front of her as they flitted along together for fifty yards, and a Starling may carry a flower to the nest where his mate is sitting. These were apparently unusual activities but Weaverfinches and Waxbills commonly carry a long stem when courting and Bowerbirds place appropriately coloured flowers and other objects in their bowers. The male Adélie Penguin proposes by presenting a pebble or even some snow (fig.22)!

Sometimes a number of Blackbirds assemble for a peculiar

*Fig. 10. Starling carrying a flower to his nest.*

social display, which I have seen performed on the roof of a shed as well as on the ground. Probably the motivation is aggressive rather than sexual or social. The display hints at how arena or 'lek' displays may have evolved (Chapter 14). Many birds perform social displays, sometimes meriting to be called 'dances' — among them Oystercatchers, Black Guillemots (plate 7) and cranes of various species. Such displays, which in some cranes amount to 'antics', also arise from mingled motives.

**Chaffinch pair-formation**

Chaffinches are gregarious in winter, sometimes mingling with other species of finch or Yellow Buntings. Single-sex flocks may be formed but occasionally Chaffinches roost in pairs, so pair-formation may not always follow a stereotyped pattern. The extent to which cocks definitely establish territories early in the year may depend on the weather. It is evident that males taking up such territories and singing there are unmated. Sexual chases occur when a female appears and the cock poses in various ways to show off his bright plumage. He may move around, tilting his body away from hers, or perch, with crest erected, turning slowly from side to side, exhibiting the white patches on his wings, or strut with his pink-suffused breast protruding. Prior to coition the female behaves as many other small birds do, quivering her drooping wings and elevating her tail.

**The pairing of Yellow Wagtails**

Cock Yellow Wagtails arrive in Britain from Africa in April and, at first, defence of territory is feeble. Individuals may fly off and join others for a while and then return, as Yellow Buntings are also apt to do. When a female flies close to a male both utter a disyllabic call and the cock runs around with wings drooped and bright yellow breast feathers puffed out. She knows him to be a male by these feathers but may make no response. Acquiescence indicates consent. When the birds have become well acquainted, the cock may precede coition by hovering over his mate or he may perform repeatedly a beautiful song-flight with vivid breast and throat feathers erected, wings vibrating as he trills. When the female is ready for coition she crouches, lowers her wings and raises her tail, twirling around several times, and her mate mounts. Only after about ten days is the first egg laid.

**Herring Gull pair-formation**

Herring Gulls generally return to the colony used the previous year and sometimes to the actual breeding site. Resort to an earlier breeding area is typical of a considerable number of species, including the Common Tern, Swallow and Redstart. Many Herring Gulls arrive at the colony already paired. Indeed, like quite a number of large marine and other birds, they seem, circumstances permitting, to mate for life. After mutual association, birds not already acquainted recognise each other individually. During courtship the females take the initiative by walking around the favoured male. He calls, stretches out his neck, walks a few yards and both make half-hearted building movements. He may

*Fig. 11. Spoonbill with crest erected in display.*

twist his neck back and forth and then the female replies by tossing her head. She walks before him and may momentarily grasp his beak — a gesture characteristic of some other species. His neck swells and he points his head downwards, regurgitating food, which she gobbles up. As time goes on conjugal feeding decreases and copulations increase at the areas where a number of birds assemble. In contrast to some other species, spectators do not try to interfere.

**Summary of elements in pair-formation**

These examples illustrate most of the elements involved in pair-formation and bird courtship: the establishment of territory by the male, utterance of song or calls, the approach of the female, hesitation, conflicting impulses, exhibition by the male of his adornments, fidgeting with objects, acceptance, sexual chases, song-flights, courtship feeding, the crouching of the female and consummation. Some of these elements may be omitted or others, such as nest-building movements, included, but the complexities of bird courtship have yet to be described.

# 4. Courtship chasing

When a bird is seen chasing another we may too readily assume that the owner of a territory is expelling an intruder, but sexual pursuits figure in the courtship procedure of many birds. The pursued individual may not be a male avoiding attack but a female 'leading on' the pursuer. In many situations, sexual or predatory, flight invites pursuit. A show of reluctance may increase a male's ardour and in sexual situations coyness can be stimulatory.

**The courtship chases of some small birds**

An ardent bunting, pipit or chat utters a specific call, approaches the female, stretches his neck, bows and raises or depresses his expanded tail — and when she flies he follows her quickly. They scurry about among the bushes or herbage as if in vigorous play but they are stimulating each other and so bringing their sexual rhythms into harmony. The birds are already paired but courtship continues until they are ready to copulate. A cock Whitethroat, already established in his territory, singing and frolicking in flight above the bushes, may be visited in turn by several females. He may sing as he chases and entices each one and yet be unsuccessful. He starts a nest and may still remain unpaired but there comes a day when he goes around silently except for a frequently uttered quiet call. He performs his miniature aerial dance, sings in a desultory way and is seen chasing a female in courtship flight. They arrive where he has built a nest or laid a foundation and he may pull suggestively at some of the material. A day or two later she lines the nest if sufficiently complete, and soon afterwards lays the first egg. Thus when male and female elicit adequate reactions in one another pairing occurs — physiological condition and behavioural responses are correlated.

**Duck courtship**

The courtship of ducks is more easily observed than the activities of small birds in dense herbage and so much is known about it. A number of drakes are attracted to a female Shoveler and individuals try to lead her away, turning the backs of their heads to her. One utters *took, totook* calls, turning sideways and then fluttering a short distance. During a hovering flight he makes a rattling noise with his wings. Such instrumental or mechanical noises during bird courtships are commoner than is generally realised. He may perform thus several times or another drake may oust him. When the duck flies off with the drake the pair-bond is established.

The American Black Duck pursues the female over land and water, nipping at her back and tail feathers in his efforts to force her down in his territory. Many species make pumping movements with head and neck. The Mallard duck swims beside a drake and he responds with displacement-drinking and preening behind and underneath a wing, thus displaying the coloured area. When a duck favours a drake she makes dipping movements with her bill — another common displacement activity among aquatic birds — and she chases him. Drakes may pursue birds leaving their nests and a number may harry a duck. Some observers speak of her being 'raped' — an undesirably emotive expression. The courtship of this common bird is complex and variable — a reminder that we have to be wary of generalisations.

# 5. Mutual and reciprocal ceremonies

**Imitative and collective behaviour**

Birds readily imitate one another. Everybody knows that parrots can learn and repeat scraps of human speech as well as other sounds. Mynahs, too, are experts at repeating words and phrases. Birds often incorporate what they hear other birds sing in their own songs and a number sing duets. Imitative action is common. An individual, feeding in a flock, flies up with his companions when one sights a predator, and among the most impressive sights a naturalist can see are the corporate manoeuvres of large flocks of Starlings or wading birds. Some large migratory birds, such as

*Fig. 12. Canada Geese migrating in flight formation.*

geese, travel in V-shaped formation. In Australia flights of up to twenty thousand Budgerigars may be seen, the flocks separating, then coming together, darkening the sky as the extinct Passenger Pigeon multitudes used to do in North America. Immense flocks of Quelea, which settle to breed in Africa where there is good foraging, are a menace to agriculture. Usually the flocking of vast hordes occurs in species which roam around, breeding where and when foraging is easy. Flamingoes, which breed in colonies, may omit nesting in years when the organisms on which they feed are scarce. Social facilitation — the tendency to act as others do — can be highly important in encouraging courtship and breeding in some species. The presence of another bird in an adjoining cage may so stimulate a female dove that she lays eggs.

Mimicry is prominent in the courtship, greeting and connubial ceremonies of many species. By acting together or reciprocally male and female are able to establish *rapport* and coordinate their sexual rhythms — become better acquainted and maintain harmony and a close relationship.

Mutual ritual is performed especially by birds with little or no perceptible difference in outward appearance between the sexes and is particularly characteristic of large aquatic species. Perhaps some can afford to make themselves conspicuous on the water as they can elude raptors by diving. Moreover, their size and, in some species, long pointed or massive beaks, adapted for fishing, deter would-be attackers. Gannets stretch up their beaks and 'fence' with them. There are various species with strikingly imitative displays in which the pair behave like mirror images of each other; only a few can be mentioned here.

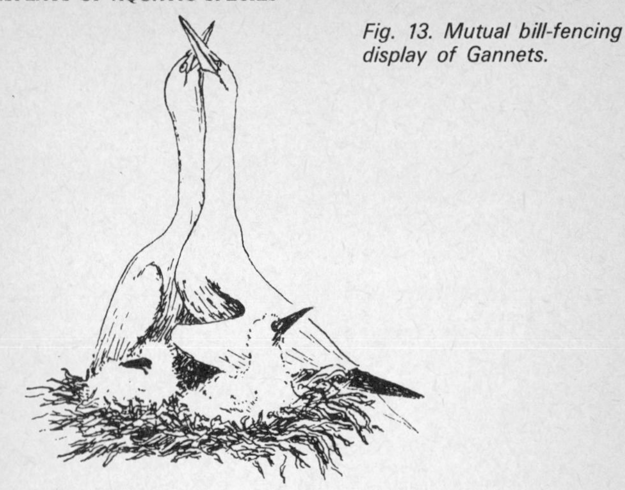

*Fig. 13. Mutual bill-fencing display of Gannets.*

**The displays of some aquatic species**

Pairs of Red-throated Diver, delicately tinted and streamlined, rear up dramatically and swiftly paddle over the surface of the lake in a stiff penguin-like posture which looks like an attempt to stand to attention while racing! Either singly or together a pair may throw themselves upside-down two or three times with legs kicking in the air. When I alarmed a Great Northern Diver approaching its nest — or rather two eggs, for no nest is made — it reared upright with wild cries. Pair-formation in this species involves mutual activity, the male leading the female to his territory, both gliding down with wings uplifted in V position. Mutual displays include the bill-dipping characteristic of ducks and grebes, and sudden dual races together, sometimes preceded by the wild hallooing which is among the most romantic and unforgettable sounds in nature. When Black-throated Divers change places on the eggs the incoming bird settles beside its mate and both participate in ceremonial head-waving.

Mutual aquatic display is performed by American Western Grebes. The birds face each other and erect their crests while their eyes bulge and a 'buzzing growl' is uttered. They dip their beaks swiftly into the water and race together, mirror images of each other a few feet apart, presenting an extraordinary spectacle as their bodies are almost vertical to the surface and their necks are held S-shaped. More than a couple may participate. These activities may occur away from the nests and at any time during the breeding season. This species and the Great Crested Grebe also dive for weeds and then, paddling vigorously, confront each other upstanding, exposing their glistening white bellies. Great Crested Grebes also sometimes float with their beaks a few inches apart, shaking their heads with chestnut tippets spread — a lovely sight. The Eared Grebe also performs 'penguin-racing' and mutual confrontation.

Similarities in forms of display provide evidence of the relationships between species but must be treated with caution. Fulvous Tree Ducks enact aquatic antics comparable in some respects with those of grebes. After copulating male and female rear up close together, treading water with necks drawn in and breasts thrust forward.

Among the most remarkable bird displays are the aerial manoeuvres of the Chiloe Wigeon, a South American species studied by W. H. Hudson. A dozen or more fly to a great height, pairs alternately drawing apart and closer together, the drakes whistling and the ducks uttering lower-pitched, measured calls. As the pairs come together they strike each other's wings so vigorously that the slaps can be heard far below.

**The displays of waxwings, Hawfinch, barbets and toucans**

The Cedar Waxwing pursues the female in wide circular flights which end with the pair perching close together on a branch, moving back and forth. Every time they come near enough they touch beaks, as courting Hawfinches sometimes do. The cock may fly off and pluck a brightly coloured berry; then, perching close to his partner, he passes it to her. But she does not eat it; she returns the gift — and so it may be exchanged back and forth a dozen or more times. Eventually it is returned to him and he drops it — its value lies only in establishing mutual feeling between the pair. The European Waxwing, which visits Britain during hard winters and may be seen feeding on cotoneaster and holly berries, performs in much the same way.

African barbets execute a kind of song and dance together, the male swaying from side to side as he sings a bubbling song, while

*Fig. 14. Weed-confrontation display of Great Crested Grebes.*

*Fig. 15. Toucan picking berries.*

his mate bobs up and down uttering clinking notes. A considerable number of other species sing duets.

Toucans have huge brightly coloured bills with which they preen one another and pick berries from slender twigs. An individual will pass such food to its mate.

**Greeting ceremonies**

Pairs of breeding birds, especially large species with powerful pointed beaks, may perform a greeting ceremony when one returns to its mate on the nest. This can be readily observed at the nest of White Storks. I watched it being performed on the roof of the priest's house in a Yugoslavian village. The bird stretches its neck until it almost touches its back and then brings its head forward and downward, rattling its mandibles. The courting female Cormorant adopts a somewhat similar posture. Such greeting ceremonies usually have affinities with the courtship display of the species and may be a brief recapitulation of them. The Hawfinch greets his mate with quivering wings and open bill. The South American Oven Bird's ritual is more elaborate. Each bird sings, one in slower tempo than the other, keeping time with slower wing-fluttering. In many species nest-relief is accompanied by some form of display.

*Fig. 16. Greeting display of White Storks.*
*Fig. 17. Greeting posture of male Cormorant.*

# 6. Display flights

**Aerial displays with songs, calls or instrumental sounds**

More than any other living creatures birds are equipped to proclaim their presence visually and vocally to convey a welcome to a potential partner and to warn or defy an intruder. Many species make 'mechanical' noises with their feathers, quills or mandibles or by pecking or drumming on a branch or the inside of a hole in a tree-trunk. The Snipe flies high, then dives through the air 'drumming', an instrumental sound created by the air rushing through his wings and tail. The courtship flights of birds may be silent or accompanied by calls. Some amount to aerial gymnastics. A pair of Ravens sometimes plunge down from the sky, the male occasionally turning on his back and gliding upside-down; a Peregrine has been seen to 'loop the loop' three times in succession and a Hen Harrier may perform aerial somersaults while uttering wild cries.

**Song-flights in relation to habitat**

Although song-flights are uttered by some woodland birds they are not so spectacular as the performances of species in more open habitats. Like other types of display, they are elements in a network of adaptations to habitat, food supply, pair-bond and so forth. The Skylark mounts vertically from the fields; the Calandra Lark, a Mediterranean species breeding in rough pastures, circles around the perimeter of his territory singing a prolonged melody, pleasant to listen to in the bare Camargue of southern France. The Black Lark of the Russian steppes flies in lower circles and the Crested Lark frequents villages and roadsides across the Channel so that even the passing motorist may notice a cock making his

*Fig. 18. Snipe in drumming flight.*

brief low song-flights. The Shorelark flies in switchback undulations but its finest songs are uttered perched on a boulder or the ground.

## Song-flights of some northern birds

The relationship between song-flights, habitat, food supply and pair-bond is particularly apparent in the Arctic and Subarctic. Where vegetation is low birds can make themselves doubly conspicuous over a wide area by singing or calling on the wing and in relatively harsh environments where foraging is sometimes time-consuming it may be advantageous thus to announce the annexation of a spacious territory and invite a female to share it.

The pairing display of the Knot is exquisite. The male mounts singing, then glides down with stiff wings and tail outspread; again he mounts, visible only when the sunlight gleams on his golden breast and light-coloured, rapidly vibrating wings. His calls become lower in tone and at last they cease as he drops with stiff, uptilted wings to the snow-covered ground.

In an area of marshy tundra in Lapland I watched a Spotted Redshank rise, calling *chup, chup, chup,* to a height of about fifty feet, then dive and zig-zag exposing the pale under-surface of his wings and white underparts. Not far away a Lapland Bunting was flying, wings outstretched and tail expanded, poised to expose the dark breast coloration to any female below. The brief song consisted of pleasant, rapidly uttered notes.

In the same area a Red-spotted Bluethroat was performing his display — ascending about ten feet and then diving into cover; but sometimes the bird would fly calling *chink, chink. . .,* then zigzag fluting *tlui, tlui. . .,* and plane down with wings and tail widely spread, exhibiting his splendid coloration. An unpaired male also spiralled around a small tree, alighting near the summit.

In northern regions as well as further south the Wheatear performs song-flights but in Cyprus a male has been seen flying back and forth repeatedly pouring forth song over the female. The Rufous Bush Robin of southern Europe and North Africa volplanes with uptilted wings and postures before the female (plate 2). Thus courtship flight-song is adaptive in harsh, open environments both north and south. It seems that the main function of such aerial songs is to attract and stimulate the female, but commonly they may be also defensive. Trilling a tinkling song, a Temminck's Stint in Lapland displayed with quivering wings at an intruder and chased it around the islet on which the nest was situated.

When comparing the courting behaviour of northern birds with that of birds in Britain and further south we need to remember that in continuous daylight birds can forage over longer hours and although the season is short there are gluts of food for some species, including Temminck's Stint, so making monogamy unadaptive. (page 49).

### Song-flights and predation

Birds nesting on tundra, moorland or desert are in danger from flying predators when they leave the ground where many, especially waders, are concealed by their dull coloration. The conspicuous Lapwing is an exception as it breeds where there is normally some concealing vegetation and it is agile and powerful enough to defy most raptors. The Merlin is the chief enemy of small birds nesting in open country, such as the Skylark and Meadow Pipit, but predators preserve the vigour of the stock by eliminating the less fit. I accidentally disturbed a Whimbrel from her nest in Lapland and blamed myself for being responsible for her imminent death when a Gyrfalcon suddenly appeared and plunged down on her — but in the nick of time she swerved and the raptor missed. I expected the Whimbrel to dive into the scanty cover but instead, suicidally as I thought, she flew still higher. The Gyrfalcon put forth an immense effort, mounted above the Whimbrel, plunged again, and once more was cheated as she swerved at the critical moment. So it went on until both birds were specks in the sky — but the raptor was outmanoeuvred and flew off hungry. So during the Whimbrel's courtship flight performed in company with the female, planing down in a spiral and occasionally turning a sideways somersault, the birds are agile enough to evade any predator.

### The Woodcock's display-flight

Standing in a wood at dusk you may see the dark form of a Woodcock weaving between tree-trunks or above the tree-tops, flying slowly and emitting a hoarse call, an odd hesitation occurring in his wing beat. Sometimes as many as five join in and chase each other in erratic flight. A female may be pursued but she may lurk in the undergrowth and call the male down. At least in some areas polyandry prevails, correlated with an excess of males.

### The display-flights of hummingbirds

Instances of beautiful song-flights can be cited from all parts of the world. Naturally hummingbirds, being so vividly coloured and agile on the wing, are star performers. Usually the male displays before the female. The Allen Hummingbird flies slowly to and fro as if suspended at the end of a huge pendulum. The Broad-tailed swoops back and forth in an open U, rising to fifty or sixty feet. As he dives downward the air rushing through slots at the tips of his primary feathers creates a rattling whistle. Two Jacobins may display in front of a female, flying aloft and then descending

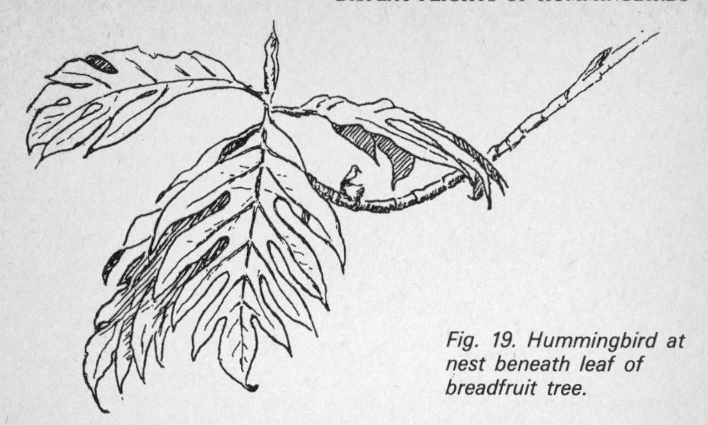

*Fig. 19. Hummingbird at nest beneath leaf of breadfruit tree.*

slowly with white tail feathers widely spread. Racket-tailed Hummingbirds hover together uttering clicking notes. One clings to a branch while the other performs a mazy aerial dance; then they reverse their roles. The remarkable tail is moved around, sometimes tilted forward almost touching the bird's head. Males of Longuemare's Hermit Hummingbird assemble, each on his chosen perch, and display throughout the day. An individual executes an elaborate aerial dance when a female appears. Besides the humming of the rapidly beating wings some species can also create a clapping sound, apparently caused by an irregularity in the wing-beats; others chirp during their display.

Hummingbirds have long beaks and protractile tongues enabling them to probe into flowers for nectar and insects. The nest may be placed beneath a large leaf. Usually all domestic duties are performed by the female.

## 7. Courtship and connubial feeding

It is sometimes useful to have terms distinguishing between feeding the partner before and during pair-formation and such feeding after the pair has been formed, but procedures vary and a clear distinction between courtship feeding and connubial or conjugal feeding cannot be made. The presentation of food by the male to the female occurs in so many families of birds — and also in insects — that the choice of examples must be arbitrary.

Tengmalm's Owl carries prey to the cavity he has chosen and this induces the female to select it; the Kingfisher and various tern species present fish. Food-begging by the Laughing Gull is a normal prelude to copulation. A Corncrake, deceived by a mounted specimen, made twenty-three attempts to copulate and then fetched a caterpillar and presented it to the unresponsive dummy! A Roller has been seen offering food and copulating in Africa some three thousand miles from its breeding area. Courtship feeding may graduate into conjugal feeding in a number of species, among them the Great Tit and the Chaffinch. The cock Chaffinch continues to bring food to his mate even when there are nestlings but she passes it to the young, as I have noticed is usual with the Goldfinch. Rooks feed their mates well into the incubation period but curtail the preliminary displays performed earlier at the nest.

Conjugal feeding reaches an extreme in hornbills. The Silvery-cheeked species walls herself into a nest-hole using a mixture of earth and saliva, and there she stays for more than a hundred days, fed by her mate, who is constant for life. Towards the end of the incubation period he may bring fruit, berries and even flowers!

*Fig. 20. Hornbill at nest.*

Male Starlings (Fig 10) and Herring Gulls also may bring flowers to the nest when the female is incubating.

**The courtship feeding of terns**

Courtship feeding may be readily observed by any patient bird-watcher visiting a nesting colony of any of the five species of tern regularly breeding in Britain — Common, Sandwich, Arctic, Roseate and Little. Among Common Terns and other species it may be important in sex recognition. The female begs for the little fish and the male offers it tentatively. He erects his tail, half spreads his wings, points his beak upwards with the fish dangling and steps around ceremoniously. She receives it but, like the Cedar Waxwing, may return it. The fish may be torn in two. The ceremony is a means whereby the birds come to an understanding. Among terns food-presentation is a pre-nuptial ceremony. Such behaviour may be regarded as an appeasement ritual, providing time and opportunity for the female to realise that the male's sharp beak does not constitute a menace. Fish presentation, like the courtship offerings of some other species, may have more than ceremonial significance. Fish can be capricious in their shoaling, so it may indicate that food for the young is likely to be available and thus stimulate pairing up.

# 8. Coition

As a number of factors, physiological, social and environmental, are involved in courtship, species differ greatly in regard to the period before the union is consummated. Among common passerine species pairs may be established weeks or even months before copulation occurs, and it may continue after the female has been incubating for some days. A Great Tit will visit the nestbox where his mate is sitting and pounce on her when she emerges in the morning. A female Snow Bunting may invite coition before the young have left the nest but it is unusual for this species to have a second brood in its more northerly breeding quarters where the climate is extreme.

Female birds have definite solicitation procedures. Although the male Wren is usually the more ardent of the two a female may perch on an exposed branch and utter a squeal which is heard at no other time. In this, as in most passerine species, coition usually takes place where the birds are concealed — a necessary precaution, although exceptions occur.

Mallard ducks and some other aquatic species copulate on the water. After facing each other making pumping movements of neck and head, the female extends her neck, lowers her body and is mounted by the drake, grasping her nape feathers. After coition they swim together, the male with neck low, the female dipping her head in the water. She quacks and he utters a lisping call. Bowerbirds copulate in the bower (plate 15).

A few species copulate in the air. Gilbert White, as long ago as 1774, noticed that Swifts do so: 'If any person would watch them of a fine morning in May, as they are sailing around at a great height from the ground he would see, every now and then, one drop on the back of another, and both of them sink down together for many fathoms with a loud piercing shriek. This I take to be the juncture when the business of generation is carrying on.'

In most species the female adopts an invitatory posture when ready for coition, squatting with wings drooped and tail elevated (plate 15). She may also, like the Wren, utter an invitatory call. A sexual pursuit may terminate in this way but it is not unusual for a male to alight on a female's back without matters proceeding further. A sixteenth-century Indian writer referred to 'the sparrow, a bird which enjoys the female some ten or twenty times in succession', but in such situations the male is trying to consummate. As among human beings sexual synchronisation is not always easily attained.

Birds are fragile creatures and in general they are averse to bodily contact unless intimate relations have been established or the warmth engendered by roosting together makes it advantageous. Various species of cormorant, gannet, spoonbill and related birds cosset, nibble each other's plumage and even twine their necks together (plates 3, 4 and 14) but these rituals are formalised and sometimes the culmination of prolonged courtship. Among higher animals, notably man, courtship involves reconciliation between the impulses of self-assertion and self-surrender, though no bird has self-consciousness as we experience it.

# 9. Incongruous courting and nesting activities

Excitement may stimulate a bird to act in an incongruous way. A Gannet, alarmed by my presence, picked up scraps of seaweed and dirt from the nest and apparently swallowed them. Disquieted birds have been known to destroy their own eggs. A Herring Gull in conflict with another may tear at potential nest-material, but this, like some other types of displacement activity, has acquired signal significance and become ritualised as a threat. Even during the changeover at the nest, a sitting Common Tern's tension may be such as to stimulate it to pick up nest-material. Similarly, at this juncture Stone Curlews may exchange a pebble. Excitement

*1. Displaying Kakapo at his 'scrape' or 'bowl'. He holds a twig in his bill, a form of displacement activity. Fiordland, New Zealand.*

*2. Male Rufous Bush Robin gyrating and displaying before the female with outspread wings and expanded decorative tail. Iberian Peninsula.*

*3. Australian Gannets. Mutual preening. Cat Island, Bass Strait.*

*4. Grey-headed Albatrosses. Mutual billing. Courting birds thus indicate to one another that their powerful bills are not going to be used aggressively. Macquarie Island, Southern Ocean.*

*5. Wandering Albatrosses. The climax of the display between male and female. During this both birds scream and yell. South Georgia.*

*6. Royal Albatrosses. A male displays to two females. The males of this species and of the Wandering Albatross establish territories and are then approached by several females. Campbell Island, Southern Ocean.*

*7. Black Guillemots. After their aquatic manoeuvres or 'dances' a party may fly around and alight on rocks, where one bird may totter after another and force it to retreat. As they call the vermilion interior of their gapes is exhibited. Northern Ireland.*

*8. Magellanic Penguins. A male in the 'ecstatic posture' uttering his braying call before a nesting hollow occupied by a female and chick. His neck bands are displayed to maximum advantage. Patagonia.*

*9. A Black and White Manakin removing a leaf from his 'court'. The 'dance' is conducted between the saplings on right and left. Trinidad.*

*10. Lyrebird singing and displaying on his 'dancing mound'. Australian Dandenongs.*

*11. Golden Bowerbird. A male decorating his courtship bower. Australia.*

*12. Satin Bowerbirds. The male has enticed the female into his bower and is courting her. Australia.*

*13. Greater Bowerbird. The male poses holding a bleached bone as he twists his head to expose his nape and bright cerise crest through the bower to the watching female. Queensland, Australia.*

14. *Royal Spoonbills. Mutual preening. Australia.*

15. *Satin Bowerbirds copulating in the male's bower. Australia.*

due to success in driving away intrusive Blue Tits has been seen to stimulate a Nuthatch to begin building.

Probably the impulse to transfer motivation to an inanimate object may account for some of the more remarkable forms of courtship and nesting behaviour, as, for example, the building of so-called 'bowers' by Bowerbirds and the collecting of objects to decorate them (plates 11, 12 and 13). The 'incubator' constructed by brush turkeys may have evolved as the result of such motivation transference. The male Mallee Fowl of Australia makes a mound in which the fermentation of decaying material provides warmth for the eggs. He devotes ten months to building and tending it, controlling the temperature by removing or replacing layers. The intervals between egg-laying and the number of eggs laid are apparently regulated by the amount of food available for the female. The young dig their way out and can fly within twenty-four hours. They are quite independent of their parents.

## 10. Presentation of nest-material during courtship

The male Grey Heron perches on a branch which he has chosen as the nest-site and displays conspicuously, stretching high his neck, bending low and making snapping sounds with his mandibles. Other birds are attracted but he keeps them away. Later he may defend only a small area immediately around the nest. His posturing warns males to keep off, but sooner or later a female ventures to approach and gradually overcomes his opposition. He reassures her by holding his beak low as if he were fishing. When he offers her a stick and she builds it into the nest the ceremony has much of the significance attached to the acceptance of an engagement or wedding ring (plates 1, 13).

The male Blue Heron, an American species, acts in a rather similar manner, at first driving the female away and even making half-hearted stabs at her, but eventually they pass their bills over each other's plumage, billing and nibbling the feathers, as also do many other large water birds such as Australian Royal Spoonbills (plate 14). The flightless Cormorant may wind its neck around its partner's in a kind of embrace.

The Roseate Spoonbill, which I have watched in Florida, threatens an approaching bird by shaking a branch in his bill, an action reminiscent of the Blackbird's intimidatory display, and stoops with wings raised, revealing the bright red under-surface — another example of the widespread use of concealed coloration to increase the effect of display; but a female persists tentatively, the birds bill each other, stick presentation occurs, and the pact is sealed.

*Fig. 21. Male Grey Heron's invitation display.*

A male Black Skimmer walks up to the selected female carrying nesting material. She approaches coyly, seizes it with an upward jerk, and then they copulate. A female Southern Cormorant at her nest in a tree pulls at twigs after assuming the solicitation posture with tail erect and neck twisted grotesquely until it almost touches her back — an attitude also adopted by the courting Shag. After coition she resumes this posture and her suitor picks up scraps and offers them to her.

There are many species in which the presentation of gifts, usually nest-material, or the manipulation of such material is a feature of courtship. An Adélie Penguin may lay a pebble or some snow at the feet of the bird he is wooing. Apparently he is unable to distinguish its sex until it reacts pugnaciously or joins him in upward bill-pointing, neck-embracing and calling. Magellanic Penguins perform comparable nebbing but the male's most imposing display is when he stands upright with wings extended and the black bands across his neck exposed (plate 8).

*Fig. 22. Adelie Penguin 'proposing' by presenting a pebble.*

# 11. Nest-invitation displays

Male birds may make nesting preparations ranging from crude scrapes to complete nests, though lining is nearly always left to the female. However, nest-building is frequently the female's responsibility. In some species both cooperate. A cock Greater Whitethroat builds a nest foundation or nest before the female arrives and then dances up a few feet in flight-song near her. If she is responsive she is led to the site and he may help her to complete the nest. As already mentioned, Tengmalm's Owl lures the female by carrying prey to the chosen cavity. The male Scops Owl enters and taps inside the hole, as a number of other tree-trunk nesting birds do. Petrels of various species call at night from their burrows and bill each other.

Migratory birds which nest in cavities and cannot hack out their own have special difficulties because residents, such as tits, may have pre-empted suitable accommodation. The provision of nestboxes by bird-lovers and foresters has shown that shortage of nest-sites is responsible for the low numbers of some species in otherwise suitable habitats. The Willow Tit and Siberian Tit are able to range further north in Europe than any other species because they can easily hack out nest-holes in rotten tree-trunks. I have noticed that in Lapland the former takes advantage of tree-trunks which have decayed at snow level. Because of the readiness with which some species, such as tits, Pied Flycatchers and American House Wrens, adopt nestboxes these are among the species most intensively studied.

**Redstart**

The cock Redstart, arriving from overseas, loses no time in acquiring a territory and nest-site. He is able to succeed even in competition with tits and Tree Sparrows and enters the cavity several times a day, sometimes remaining with his head protruding. When a female arrives he signals temptingly to her by flitting in and out. His contrasting frontal feathers and red tail make him conspicuous. As she is diffident about entering an enclosed space the cock uses various kinds of enticement. He sings loudly and hovers before the opening, enters and then glides down with tail spread, singing. When the female has approved the site she does nearly all the building. She is influenced by various environmental factors and is apt to prefer a cavity or nestbox at approximately the height at which the birds hunt insects.

**Pied and Collared Flycatcher**

The nest-attraction displays of the Pied and Collared Flycatcher are broadly similar to the Redstart's. The cock advertises the site he has secured by popping in and out, and he defends it from would-be usurpers. He may lay the nest foundation. When a potential mate appears he increases his activity and invites her by flying flamboyantly to the hole, quivering his wings and uttering high-pitched calls. He also utters a subdued song such as is sung by the Wren in similar circumstances.

**Great Tit**

The Great Tit, being a resident, often pairs up in the flock. Flocks disperse about the beginning of the year when aggressive behaviour develops. The cock chases the hen, both flying with incomplete wing-strokes and short glides. He may utter a brief warble and perch near the nest-hole, looking inside and twisting his head, making his white cheeks conspicuous. When disputes occur he assumes an erect posture with body and neck vertical, exhibiting the contrasting plumage. During skirmishes a bird may throw leaves over his back — a form of displacement activity. The female approaches tentatively, quivering her wings. When she goes inside she may peck at the wood as the male has already done — perhaps assuring herself that the cavity is solid and safe.

**Wren**

The male Wren may build as many as a dozen complete or incomplete nests and attracts a mate or mates — for in favourable habitats he is apt to be polygamous — by singing loudly and persistently while he proclaims his presence and the boundaries of his territory. Subspecies living in outlying, almost tree-less islands are monogamous — a highly significant difference, supporting the principle that easy foraging tends to encourage multiple pairing. When a roving female enters a male's territory, lured by his songs, she approaches timidly, pecking here and there as if not interested. She seldom seizes any insect or other food. The cock becomes very excited, his movements become unusually nimble, and he sings a beautiful, subdued song, popping in and out of the nest and so indicating the position of the entrance. Coyly she draws nearer and eventually enters to inspect the interior. If satisfied she begins bringing in feathers to line it. When she has settled into the nest a polygamously inclined male then concentrates on singing here and there in his territory and conducts the same procedure with another, and perhaps a third female. As females inspect and reject nests in less attractive areas, such as city suburbs, they are probably influenced in their choice not only by the male's displays and the character of his nest but also by the whole environment. They tend to settle in an area which will yield adequate food for a brood.

**Weaverbirds**

The males of some polygamous weavers, such as the Masked Weaver, outdo the Wren in industry, constructing many complete and incomplete nests in a season. They call attention to them by uttering cries while clinging to them or, more correctly, the hanging nests being very conspicuous, they call to induce females to choose them.

**Oropendola**

The Oropendola is a large, oriole-like bird of the American tropics with a bill adapted to seize fruit and insects, to sip nectar and to weave the compact pouched nest, similar to but larger than the hanging nests of some weavers. The fibrous plaited 'rope' on which it is suspended may be four or five feet long. Oropendolas breed in colonies and at first glance the highly conspicuous pensile nests appear precariously placed, unconcealed, swinging in the trade wind; but such nests, suspended from thin outermost twigs, are inaccessible to even very agile climbers such as coatis and monkeys. However, Oropendolas do not escape persecution as a large cowbird, the Rice Grackle, lays in the nest and a flycatcher is able to evict the owners and breed in them — an illustration of how delicately poised are a bird's adaptations. Apparently risking parasitisation is more advantageous than being at the mercy of tree-climbing mammals such as howler monkeys.

In contrast to weavers, the females are the nest-builders, paying no attention to the males who come ogling them with blue eyes, body feathers fluffed and tails twitching, uttering spluttering cries. Only when the nest is complete does the female respond and caress an insistent male, fondling his crown feathers. He follows her everywhere, only mildly vocal, for his aim has been achieved and she is his — but only for the time being. After she has laid her two eggs he transfers his attentions to another bird in the colony and she is left to incubate and rear the young. By human standards his behaviour might appear callous, for all the work is left to

*Fig. 23. Oropendola at nest.*

her, yet it seems to be in the best interests of the species as females outnumber males by five or six to one. As all of them are not available at the same time they can be fertilised in succession, and this extension of breeding permits the exploitation of the forest's varied food supply over a longer period than would otherwise be possible. The interests of the race are served.

# 12. Diverse types of pair-bond

Among birds there are many exceptions to a monogamous pair-bond. Even within monogamy there are variations; a cock bird may take a different mate for a second brood and in some species it is not unusual for an additional bird or birds to help feed the young, as at a Long-tailed Tit's nest — usually an individual from an earlier nesting. Life-long relationships are recorded of some larger species as different as Ravens and Emperor Penguins. Great Tits are believed to pair for life — which in such small birds is short — but an exceptional male may be bigamous. A Wren may live five or six years. We have already noted that the Wren is monogamous in austere northern habitats, such as Shetland and St Kilda, but tends to be polygamous in lush English or continental woodland. It has been estimated that in a Kittiwake colony sixty-four per cent of the birds nested with the same partner in a later season. Sexual synchronisation can be more readily established and breeding activities more efficient in such circumstances although there is some evidence that after a few years the number of young reared by pairs of some species may decrease. The nature of the sexual relationship between birds is such as to give primacy to the needs of the young. As a rule birds time breeding activities so that food for the young will be in good supply.

**Monogamy: the Emperor Penguin**

Among birds monogamy is naturally common as, in most circumstances, the young are best tended when the pair cooperate. A number of large aquatic species remain permanently paired. The Emperor Penguin, largest of all marine birds and therefore needing abundant food, breeds in the most severe conditions endured by any bird — on the Antarctic ice in the bitter cold, blizzards and darkness of winter. The males, each with a single egg on his feet warmed in his lower breast feathers, huddle together for the two months of incubation. When the chick hatches it is fed with a crop secretion until the female returns. She takes over and the male then goes to sea, recoups the energy lost and returns to feed and tend the chick.

**The Oilbird**

Another monogamous species living in extreme conditions is the Oilbird or Guacharo of South America and Trinidad, which spends its life in darkness. The birds fly out of the caverns in which they nest only at dusk and seek fruit on forest trees, sometimes miles away. In appearance the Oilbird is like a very large nightjar with a hooked beak. It was a strange experience to penetrate the depths of one of these caves, wading in the stream which runs through it, the banks of which were lined with the foot-high pale stems of seedlings sprung from nuts dropped by the birds. As we advanced the long-winged birds appeared momentarily in the light of our torches and the clamour increased until it was a loud chorus of snarling cries. These were intermingled with clicks, the birds' echo-location adaptation. At the end of the long subterranean passage we came on the nests — stumpy, foot-high cylinders of hardened regurgitated mush. In the concave summit of each rested two or three fat, featherless, hooked-billed chicks.

The eggs are incubated for rather more than a month and the parents take turns. Another four months are needed to rear the young and nesting is so timed that food is available in greatest variety while they are in the nest. During the year clutch-size decreases in correlation with decreasing food. Without an enduring pair-bond the young could not be reared. The pair retain the nest from year to year. The nightjar-like appearance of these birds is correlated with their nocturnal feeding behaviour as what would normally be considered camouflage plumage has little or no advantage in the caves. In the tree-tops where the Oilbirds pick off fruit while in flight, owls, the only relevant predators, are unlikely to attack them because of their owl-like coloration. To a minor extent crabs interfere with the nesting colonies and occasionally eat the chicks but man is the only predator raiding and sometimes destroying them. He collects and boils them for their oil in spite of superstitions which linger around these 'Diablotins' or 'Devil-birds'.

**Types of pair-bond among waders**

The waders, a large group including species adapted to very various climatic and ecological conditions, exemplify a range of different forms of pair-bond related to their habitat requirements. The majority, including the Ringed Plover of our shingle shores, the Stone Curlew of Breckland and the Lapwing, breeding on rough grassland, are monogamous, but the European and American Woodcock are not. As these birds are nocturnal or crepuscular there is some uncertainty about their domestic affairs but territory-holding males of the American species copulate with any responsive female. The favourite breeding haunts are moist patches in woodland where there is rich foraging. Woodcock are equipped with sensitive, flexible-tipped mandibles so that they can seize worms underground and thus exploit a source of food not available to any other species. An individual may eat its own weight of food in twenty-four hours and the young are nearly full grown when rather more than three weeks old — an important adaptation in woodland where predators abound. Moreover the female is able to carry the chicks between her legs. Between April and July the male's weight may fall from 360 to 263 grams — an indication of the energy expended in his displays. Thus in the American Woodcock — and probably the European species — a multiple pair-bond is associated with a special adaptation for feeding and rapid maturation of the young and exceptional predator-frustrating behaviour.

**Multiple pair-bonds**

In the Arctic summer there is continuous daylight, a sudden flush of life in spring and a shorter breeding season than in lower latitudes. The plenitude of insect life in some regions is such that naturalists who go bird-watching without veil and gloves are liable to be very uncomfortable. One of the waders nesting in Lapland, Temminck's Stint, has adapted to these conditions by forming polyandrous unions. The female, able readily to find plenty of food over a brief period, leaves both males to incubate and tend the chicks. Thus the females, because of the good foraging conditions, can lay two clutches in quick succession, and the young profit by the abundant food when they hatch.

One sex of quite a number of northern wading birds may take little part in incubation or brooding. Investigation may show that in some species the responsibilities undertaken by the sexes differ in accordance with climate and environment. On Bathurst Island, northern Canada, the cock Sanderling incubates and cares for the young. If circumstances are favourable and adequate food is available a second clutch is laid and the female takes responsibility for it, but in north-east Greenland both parents are attentive. The male Dotterel, nesting sparsely high on the Scottish mountains, normally performs all incubation. The females flock some distance away — leaving the nesting areas free for the males and chicks to forage. This is adaptive as the females use up much energy in producing the clutch of relatively large eggs. Successive mating, which has been noted in this species in Scotland and the Austrian Alps, favours the rearing of the maximum number of young. Two Greenshanks, mates of the same cock, have been known to lay in one nest. The Snow Bunting, a species with little in common with the Dotterel apart from breeding in comparable harsh environments, is described as polyandrous in Scotland but in Greenland the male may tend some of the young, his mate the others, but when she mates with another male these may die. In Scotland about forty-seven per cent of the females attempt to rear a second brood. Thus an uneasy compromise has been reached to secure the rearing of the maximum number of young in unfavourable conditions.

The Red-necked Phalarope is a sprightly little northern wader with distinctive feeding behaviour, performing solo spinning manoeuvres in shallow pools and seizing small organisms thus brought to the surface — procedure comparable with that of a number of species which 'paddle' on damp ground to bring up worms within reach. In Iceland, where few predators disturbed them until the disastrous introduction of the mink, I found Phalaropes almost indifferent to my presence in a breeding colony. The females are larger than the males, as in a number of other northern waders, correlated with the relatively large eggs they lay; this, in turn, is an adaptation ensuring that the chicks can soon be independent. They seek and court partners, making a high-pitched clattering with their wings as they flit over the marshy ground. After pair-formation the couples go from place to place prospecting for a nesting site and, having chosen it, the male is left to incubate. Observers differ as to whether the females mate with more than one male but in some areas individuals may do so. American naturalists report polygamy and attempted polyandry. One of these comments that Wilson's Phalaropes 'very usually maintain two establishments', which may mean that the regime resembles that of Temminck's Stint. The females are said to compete for the males. When more is known about northern waders it may be found that the pair-bond varies according to the food supply in the habitat, as in the Wren.

## 13. Habitat, pair-bond and networks of adaptation

Reviewing briefly evidence already quoted supporting the importance of the foraging procedure and its side-effects on a bird's life-style, attention may be called to the relationship between enclosed, pouch or deep hammock nests and multiple pairing. Reference has already been made to the covered nests of some non-monogamous species. Pensile hammock or pouch nests not only thwart mammalian predators but also conserve warmth. Even in the tropics heat conservation and consequent energy-saving can be advantageous when a single parent is responsible for the eggs and young. Some polygamous hummingbirds, which build nests on the stems of or suspended beneath large leaves, achieve concealment, inaccessibility and some conservation of warmth. The polygamous Wren, whose antecedents may be traced to tropical America, was pre-adapted for colder climates by making a roofed nest which could also serve as a cosy winter dormitory. The fledged young, like young woodpeckers, may return to the nest to roost and adults cluster in nests on winter nights.

Probably in some species a physiological peculiarity may have encouraged multiple pairing. The ratio of males to females may have been disturbed thus, or by predation, but in some lek species the sexes are equal in numbers. The relatively inconspicuous coloration of females as compared with males in many species suggests that this adaptation serves to protect them at the expense of their consorts. None the less evidence is accumulating indicating that a non-monogamous pair-bond is primarily related to feeding behaviour.

Of the fourteen species known to be regularly polygamous in North America thirteen breed in marshes. Such habitats provide excellent foraging for birds adapted to them. They are wide open to sunlight, and sun and water together are the great energy-givers. This is one of the reasons why the variety of organisms in the humid tropics is much greater than in temperate regions. Polygamy is most frequent in Reed Warblers among birds established in particularly favourable areas of reed-beds. Another denizen of the same reed-beds, the Bittern, may have as many as five mates.

**The Pheasant-tailed Jacana**

This tropical species is polyandrous and, like the Red-necked Phalarope and Woodcock, has an unusual way of feeding. Being long-legged with extremely elongated toes, these birds are able to run over, feed and nest on aquatic vegetation — hence the popular name 'Lily-trotter'. The female is larger than the male, as in some other polyandrous birds, and lays successive clutches of four eggs, leaving the series of males with which she copulates successively responsible for them. Climatic conditions and wet habitats render food plentiful towards the end of the rainy season when breeding occurs. The bird's adaptations enable it to avoid direct competition with other species and the chicks, being soon able to swim, dive and conceal themselves in the aquatic vegetation, are thus able to evade predators.

**Large flightless species**

South American Rheas are practically omnivorous. They feed in flocks and breeding is preceded by fighting between the mature males. A successful cock makes a nest, preferably near water, by lining a hollow and then leads females to it, displaying his white rump as an alluring signal. As many as six hens may lay in one nest. The cock broods and leads the chicks from the nest. South African Ostriches also are polygamous and catholic in choice of food. A male may have a harem of five hens, all laying in one nest. He may do most of the incubation but in south-west Africa a male and his three mates share responsibilities. Perhaps behaviour varies according to the food available. Emus, like these other large flightless birds, have a varied diet and forage widely. The male incubates and takes charge of the chicks.

Thus non-monogamous unions in these species are correlated with structural and foraging adaptations, large size, flightlessness, long necks and legs, and roaming proclivities. Consideration of their behaviour, together with that of other birds with unusual or extreme adaptations, reinforces the view that the method of foraging is fundamental to a bird's life-style, especially its form of pair-bond, and that other adaptations can be considered in relation to it.

# 14. Arena or lek displays

Some birds are extremely sociable when breeding, while others nest at a great distance from pairs of their own species. On some islands off our shores Gannets' nests are spaced a beak's reach from one another but, at the other extreme, Golden Eagles' eyries are separated by miles of moorland. A pair nesting in County Antrim brought prey from across the Irish Sea. Male and female Waxbills may incubate side by side. Village Weaverbirds build a huge communal structure with separate compartments for the nests.

A number of species engage in social displays not performed at traditional display grounds — Black Guillemots on the sea and Oystercatchers in 'piping parties' along the shore.

Communal and social behaviour are determined by various factors, including the mutual stimulation and, often, protection thus achieved, but obviously social nesting depends on the neighbourhood being such as to yield sufficient food for parents and young. The numbers of some fish-eating birds seem to have been limited in the past, not by the fish population but by the

*Fig. 24. Oystercatcher piping display*

availability of suitable cliffs and islands where the birds, especially the young, could be immune from the ravages of carnivorous mammals. Now pollution of the sea and rash exploitation of its resources have a yet more detrimental effect in some regions.

As marine species range widely over the sea and feed and breed where food is plentiful they are non-territorial, apart from defending the nest-site. Territory could be succinctly defined as 'a persistently defended area' but such a definition is inadequate as it does not define what, in the area, is defended. This is normally the breeding and foraging area so we might widen the definition by adding 'because of the food available there'. But lek display constitutes an alternative to each male, female or pair defending its feeding and nesting area. If males in an area resort to a specific small confrontation area a much larger area is available for the females to nest in and forage for themselves and their young, provided the males are not needed to incubate or tend the chicks. Hence the evolution of this form of display. The display stance, a minimal form of 'territory', may be either close to or far from the stances of other males of the species. Normally the birds are within sight of one another but, as we shall presently see, the term 'dispersed lek' is used here to describe activities in which the stances or 'courts' are far apart but such that the males can keep in touch by means of their loud utterances. Most attention will be paid to those species which assemble to display at, near or with each other on an assembly area or arena either on the ground or in trees or bushes. The females are entirely responsible for building the nest, incubating and tending the young. The term 'lek' is said to be derived from the Swedish *leka* (to play amorously), but competition prevails and in the larger species conflicts may occur. The males normally work off their pugnacity at a rendezvous where they are visited and chosen for copulation by the females. Lek display is of special interest as, although it is characteristic of relatively few species, they belong to widely different groups and live in environments as different as the Sub-arctic and tropical rain forest.

**The jousting of the Ruff**

My first experience of Ruffs at their lek was when cycling on the Dutch island of Texel. I noticed a party displaying on the road ahead. They dispersed but almost immediately reassembled after I had passed. I was informed that the birds had remained faithful to the traditional display arena even after the road had been built across it. Other lek species similarly tend to return each season to the ancestral display areas. The Ruffs' stances are only a foot or two apart and are visible as bare patches worn in the turf. There is a rank order such that, for a time, particular dominating birds are preferred by the Reeves, which may visit more than one lek, or

*Fig. 25. Reeve choosing a Ruff.*

'hill' as the arenas used to be called in England — probably because the display grounds were on slightly elevated places in the fenland.

The males' nuptial adornments, after which Ruffs are named, develop for the spring performances. They are large erectile frills, differing from individual to individual. A Reeve indicates her choice by nibbling a Ruff's feathers. The silence of the displaying birds is almost eerie as it seems so unnatural for confrontations to be conducted without vocal challenges. The absence of cries may be due to the tilting grounds being traditional and their location being advertised by the birds flying to and from them. Also loud calling would render such comparatively small birds, encumbered with ornamental frills, additionally vulnerable.

**Leks of the Blackcock and related species**

Even when a Blackcock lek is not in use the arena can be recognised by the worn areas in the moorland turf a yard or so across. The birds assemble mainly at dawn to confront each other, cock against cock, uttering sustained, almost dovelike, 'rook-ooing' and gobbling calls. In nuptial attire the Blackcock is a handsome bird with shining blue-black plumage and white undercoverts which are erected during display together with the lyre-shaped tail. The cocks advance and square up to one another like fighting Gamecocks, fluttering up together in a flurry of wings. In contrast to the Ruffs' performance there is sound and fury but rarely does one bird cripple another. Their efforts are adapted to attain or maintain dominance and the outcome is that the fittest propagate the race. When a Greyhen approaches a Blackcock he runs around with his near wing drooped, crimson-combed head held low and tail spread. Coition may occur on the male's stance.

Comparable tournaments are staged by related North American species. Assemblies on the 'strutting ground' of the Sage Grouse may number hundreds. This species, the Blue, Sharp-tailed Grouse and Greater and Lesser Prairie Chickens have coloured air-sacs, inflated during diaplay. Their arenas are frequented year after year.

**Relationship between lek displays and habitat in the grouse family in Britain**

Comparison will be confined to the behaviour of the four members of the family in Britain, and more precisely in Scotland. The Ptarmigan breeds at heights of 2200 to 4000 feet and its environment is harsh. These birds are almost entirely vegetarian and will even eat lichen or burrow into snow to feed. Monogamy prevails, as we might expect in such bleak conditions and where the guardianship of the chicks by the cock as well as the hen is important. The Red Grouse is also monogamous but inhabits lower levels, moorland and rough, boggy ground. It is mainly vegetarian, relying largely on heather but about twenty per cent of its food may be animal. For their first few weeks the chicks feed mainly on insects. Tramping across the moors, I have sometimes been startled by a cock flapping up from a rock close by and cackling *go back, go back, back, back, back, back* — the bird's normal display proclamation. During the threat display the red wattle over the eye becomes distended. Early in the season there are solo performances but as ardour increases so does competitiveness and cocks from adjoining stances may approach, displaying and crowing. Several birds may become involved and one may even strike another in flight. Ptarmigan in neighbouring territories may also quarrel. Red Grouse engage in sexual pursuits on the wing, the cock following close behind the dodging hen. When paired he advances stiffly with tail erect and covers the squatting female.

The Black Grouse prefers areas with trees near at hand, plantations with open spaces and the fringes of woods. The lek is on open ground. The birds feed on heather shoots, buds of larch and pine, wild fruits and various insects, including the pupae of ants. As they frequent woodland as well as moors their diet can be more varied than that of either Ptarmigan or Red Grouse. The largest of the four species, the Capercaillie, is a bird of coniferous woodland and may display or call on the ground or in a tree. The display includes strutting and wing-flapping leaps. Sometimes the performance may be social with a few males and females involved but, as with the Ptarmigan and Red Grouse, display stances are defended. A companion in Lapland was repeatedly attacked by a cock — evidently misdirected aggression due to sexual frustration. The Capercaillie is polygamous and its range of food is catholic — buds and shoots of conifers, bracken 'crosiers', heather flowers, berries, cereals and insects.

This survey of grouse species in the limited area, Scotland, shows that each has its ecological niche and that those of the more austere, monotonous, unwooded habitats are monogamous while the others where foraging is more varied are polygamous or promiscuous. What is true of Wren subspecies is also valid for these game birds — monogamy in harsh habitats, multiple pairing in areas with richer vegetation. We must be careful not to generalise too widely concerning the grouse family as a whole and to be wary of applying the principle of the relationship between food, pair-bond and display rashly, but it can be used to throw light on the network of adaptations in many species.

**The dances of manakins**

Some years after studying the Ruffs' lek activities I found another lek species in very different surroundings. Roaming through the beautiful rain forest on an island in Central America I heard sounds resembling those of twigs snapping beneath the paw of a large animal. As I knew a puma had been photographed nearby and a white-lipped peccary had recently injured a naturalist I was a little disquieted but when I peered through the bushes I discovered that the cracking noises were being made by a small bird hopping to and fro among the twigs a few yards away. Further investigation revealed that I had happened on the display 'court' of Gould's Manakin, a small yellow and black bird named after a nineteenth-century naturalist. This display area is kept tidy, the performer removing any leaf or twig falling to the ground below the branches perched on during the display. He flits from one to another uttering disyllabic calls. On the appearance of a green-plumaged female there is much excitement; she and the chosen male 'set to partners', rhythmically leaping across the court. These can be in groups about thirty feet apart.

At another performance in Trinidad I watched the Golden Manakin at the lek twenty-five feet up in a tree, darting here and there, facing about swiftly. His display-flights are sometimes accompanied by wing-noises and he now and then shuffles backwards along a horizontal branch. The display arenas are communal and, as is customary with some other species, are frequented from year to year. Males spend nearly ninety per cent of the daylight hours at their courts throughout much of the year, so food must be easily obtainable — an important factor in enabling such lek displays to evolve and be maintained. As with Gould's Manakin, the Black and White species, also native to Trinidad, keeps courts on the display arena free from litter — an outlet for tension pending the arrival of a female (plate 9). The males are polygamous and the females mainly promiscuous. To copulate the cock slides down a sapling on to the female's back. The breeding season coincides with the period when food is most readily obtainable and the female finds no difficulty in feeding the two chicks. There is no disparity in the numbers of the sexes. Thus, like other lek species, manakins resort to favoured places year after year for their amorous ballets and the displays are ritualised and orderly. A kind of inborn etiquette prevails.

**The displays of Cotingas**

The Cotingas, a tropical American family, include some remarkable species: the Umbrella Bird with a crest which flops over the male's head; the Three-wattled Bell-bird adorned with three fleshy spikes springing from the base of the male's bill; and the Cock of the Rock, larger than any manakin — an imposing bird with brilliant orange plumage and a prominent crest which overlaps and nearly conceals his bill. There are similarities between his dance and those of the manakins but he sometimes perches quite still in his court for several minutes — an unusual thing for any bird to do. His vivid coloration makes him conspicuous even when at rest. The Capuchinbird is the size of a small crow and, in contrast to most lek birds, dully coloured, but with feathers at the back of his head like a monk's hood — hence his name. The alternative name, Calfbird, is derived from the loud mooing calls by which he makes up for his lack of brilliant colours.

The Capuchinbird's lek is among branches about thirty feet high. One bird is dominant and two face each other some fifteen inches apart. They call alternately. Like the Cock of the Rock, a Capuchinbird may remain motionless for a long time—as much as ninety-three minutes. Such attitudes are maintained longest when another male is near. An aggressive male fluffs out his upper breast like a Pouter Pigeon, Robin or Yellow Wagtail, and a couple may move from branch to branch, dislodging one another, displacement-preening and plucking leaves and twigs — an equivalent to the court-tidying of other lek birds. In some species fidgeting with material is an aggressive display. When Jungle Fowl fight and one pecks at the ground this is not merely a way of 'letting off steam' but indicates that the bird is likely soon to resume combat.

**The displays of birds of paradise**

More than a century ago Wallace, the co-discoverer with Darwin of the principle of evolution, mentioned the displays of the Great Bird of Paradise. In *The Malay Archipelago* he wrote of their *sacaleli* or dancing parties, describing how the exquisitely adorned birds assemble in high trees, moving rapidly from branch to branch 'in great excitement, so that the whole tree is filled with waving plumes in every variety of attitude and motion. The bird itself is nearly as big as a crow, and is of a rich coffee-brown colour . . . At the time of its ecstasy the wings are raised vertically above the back, the head is bent down and stretched out, and the long plumes are raised and expanded until they form two magnificent golden fans striped with red at the base, falling off into the pale brown tint of the finely divided and softly waving points. The whole bird is then overshadowed by them, the crouching body, yellow head, and emerald green throat forming but the setting for the golden glory which waves and quivers above.' The Lesser Bird of Paradise's display is somewhat similar. Like so many other lek birds the Great Bird of Paradise practises plural mating but such relationships among birds are not indicative of disorder. In most such species the female's choice is paramount and a male's opportunities for copulating may depend on his age and rank order in the group. In some primate societies thus organised subordinates have their turn with the females and this may be true of some bird communities.

The Magnificent Bird of Paradise, resplendent with bright green iridescent breast and long curled tail feathers, displays like a number of other lek species in a forest arena from which he removes leaves, and the Blue Bird of Paradise exhibits his exquisite plumes hanging upside down from a branch. There are monogamous species but those most elaborately adorned practise plural mating. Once the degree of brilliance and elaboration of adornment together with agility in display became of selective value, the tendency for females to choose birds exhibiting these characteristics gained momentum, resulting in extravagant adornment, as occurred with Ruffs' frills, but with them evolution has been in the direction of individuality expressed by differences between these. The King Bird of Paradise not only is adorned with

*Fig. 26. Lesser Bird of Paradise displaying.*

*Fig. 27. Upside-down display of the Blue Bird of Paradise.*

tail quills ending in glittering green discs but also sings melodiously, displaying his apple-green throat. Some birds of paradise display obsessively for long periods even in the absence of other individuals. We can assume that the expenditure of so much energy indicates that their food supply is plentiful and readily obtainable.

**Dispersed lek displays**

Lek display stances can be so distant that only the very loud calls of the birds keep them in touch. (Social displays not restricted to a display stance or arena, such as those already mentioned of Blackbirds or Oystercatchers, are in a different category.) We may regard species in which the males' stances are so far apart that the birds maintain contact by means of loud cries or songs as 'dispersed lek' species but clear distinctions cannot be drawn between these and other lek birds, apart from the characteristic that their utterances are usually exceptionally loud. Large, ornate species of the Pheasant family, such as the Peacock, Peacock Pheasant and Argus Pheasant, with ocellated plumes, are polygamous or promiscuous, live in jungle and utter very loud cries at their separate stances. As already mentioned some Bitterns mate with more than one female. The 'boom' can be heard at a distances of two miles. The 'boom' of the Kakapo or Owl-parrot of New Zealand carries more than half a mile. This almost extinct, large, flightless, nocturnal parrot establishes dispersed leks comparable with those of some pheasants but each bird makes a hollow in the ground near a boulder which reflects the call. The wings and tail are maintained in a spread position and the wings are slowly raised and lowered periodically as a basking butterfly does (plate 1). The male approaches the female walking slowly backwards from his bowl, wings and tail spread and body rocking slowly from side to side. The bird in the photograph is holding a twig in his bill, probably a displacement activity due to thwarted sexual drive. The Kakapo breeds at irregular intervals of one to four years and apparently its nesting is correlated with a rapid increase in the erratic food supply.

The Ruffed Grouse of North American woodland, which stands with fanned tail drumming loudly on a log, is exceptional in being monogamous but an individual may copulate with two hens.

Male Superb Lyrebirds each establish a number of song and display stances or 'mounds' within the territory and utter songs embodying mimicries which render each song distinctive (plate 10). Like a number of bowerbird species both lyrebird species are believed to be promiscuous. Breeding is in winter when food is most abundant. The nestling is tended only by the female.

While sitting by a pool watching hippopotami in East Africa, I observed close at hand the display of Jackson's Whydah, a member of the weaver family. The male is adorned with very long tail plumes and when a female approaches he hops and flies up beside a tuft of grass around which his activities have worn a smooth ring. The visiting female might almost be said to play a game of hide and seek as she keeps to the side of the tussock away from him. Ever and anon he flaunts his tail in her face. She inspects and pecks at the tussock as if more interested in it than in him. When she flies off, as she usually does, he expresses his frustration by tearing at the grass in the ring. There may be many 'dancing rings' in an area and the females visit one or other from time to time. Their nests may be quite a long distance apart. If the tuft is removed the male continues to dance around where it was but the females no longer visit the ring. The tuft is an indispensable sex symbol and stimulant (see cover illustration).

**Bowerbirds**

Throughout we have noted the strong tendency for birds to manipulate objects around them, sometimes fidgeting with them in states of tension, sometimes using them practically for nest-building and in some situations giving them what we can only call 'symbolic' significance. The bowerbirds have developed further than Jackson's Whydah an association with an object in courtship activities by constructing this object, the so-called 'bower'. There are 'platform', 'maypole' and 'avenue' builders. Maypole-building involves the construction of a high cone of material around a sapling. The Golden Bowerbird's may be nine feet in height. The Gardener Bowerbirds of New Guinea decorate their platforms with fruit and flowers and the cock Satin Bowerbird adorns his arched arbour with various objects, flowers, feathers, paper, etc, preferring those which are blue, like his eyes (plate 12). He paints the uprights, choosing blueberries if available, squeezing them to the tip of his bill and applying the liquid to the sticks. Some observers think that this species may use a wad of fibrous material as a paint brush or palette. ('Tool-using' has been recorded of quite a number of birds — an interesting example being the Egyptian Vulture, which batters Ostrich eggs with a large stone to obtain the contents.) The Satin Bowerbird postures for months at his bower, a female looking on from time to time, but not until there is a plenitude of food available does she enter the bower and deflect the male's attention from it and its trinkets to herself, eventually assuming the invitatory posture within it (plates 12 and 15). Then she goes off to build the nest, lay and rear the young. The Greater Bowerbird poses so that his crest and coloured nape are visible to the female as she looks through the bower (plate 13).

*Fig. 28. Whooper Swans migrating.*

# Summary

As a group birds are outstanding among forms of animal life for the great variety in their structural and behavioural adaptations to terrestrial, aquatic and aerial foraging associated with highly developed visual, vocal, instrumental and tactile means of communication. Consequently their sexual displays and social relationships take manifold forms and are often of great complexity and beauty. When account is taken of the association of activity, adornment and utterance, some species have higher aesthetic appeal than any creature of any other group.

A bird's mode of foraging is basic to its life-style, involving structure, adornments, the nature of the pair-bond, territorial, courtship and breeding activities, dispersal and migratory behaviour. The foraging adaptations of birds are refined and differentiated, with each species occupying its own ecological niche, thus avoiding detrimental competition with other species or excessive exploitation of the environment — a dynamic equilibrium which, so far, has eluded mankind.

# Bibliography

There is an immense and rapidly growing literature on bird displays associated with courtship, most of it in learned journals, so I mention works in which there are extensive bibliographies: E. A. Armstrong, *Bird Display and Behaviour,* Dover, New York, 1965, and *A Study of Bird Song,* Dover, New York, 1973; also E. A. Armstrong and H. L. K. Whitehouse, 'Behavioural Adaptations of the Wren', *Biological Reviews,* Cambridge, 1977. J. C. Welty's *The Life of Birds,* Saunders, Philadelphia and London, 1975, discusses courtship as well as many other aspects of bird behaviour. E. O. Wilson's *Sociobiology,* Harvard University Press, 1976, is the most recent scientific synopsis discussing bird behaviour in the context of animal behaviour in general. *Discovering Bird Song,* in the present series by the author, Shire Publications, 1977, contains comments on songs and calls which are significant in courtship activities. *The Birds of the Western Palearctic,* ed. S. Cramp, Oxford University Press, 1977, is authoritative but only the first volume has been published. A. L. Thompson's *New Dictionary of Birds,* Nelson, 1964, is a valuable reference book.

# Index